THIS BOOK IS ABOUT

_____

PREPARED WITH LOVE BY

_____

OTHER GIFTBOOKS BY HELEN EXLEY

The Baby Blessing
My Wedding Planner
Grandmother Remembers
A Christening Gift
To a Very Special Mother
To a Very Special Grandma
Forever Your Baby Girl
Forever Your Baby Boy
Forever My Mum
Forever My Dad
Forever My Grandma
Be Happy!

This edition published 2013 for Index Books

ISBN: 978-1-84634-592-0

Published by Helen Exley®
Helen Exley Giftbooks, 16 Chalk Hill, Watford, WD19 4BG, UK.
www.helenexleygiftbooks.com

BABY
RECORD
BOOK

Forever Friends
™

Introduction

Here is a journal that enables you to keep a record
of some of the most amazing and joyful experiences in life –
your child's first weeks and years!

Write down the events as they occur –
all those happy, chaotic and hilarious moments.
Then, later on, you will be able to focus
on this time in your life and relive it all with a smile.
Babies are babies for such a short time.
Enjoy it and remember to record everything.
Glue in lots of photographs and your child's first drawings,
and rewrite headings so that they're just right for you.

This book will make a precious memento
for both you and your child – and perhaps, one day,
even for your grandchildren.

Contents

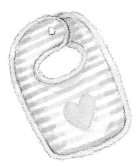

Your Birth

PLACE

DATE

WEIGHT

WHAT YOU LOOKED LIKE

THINGS WE WILL NEVER FORGET

PHOTO HERE

First visitors

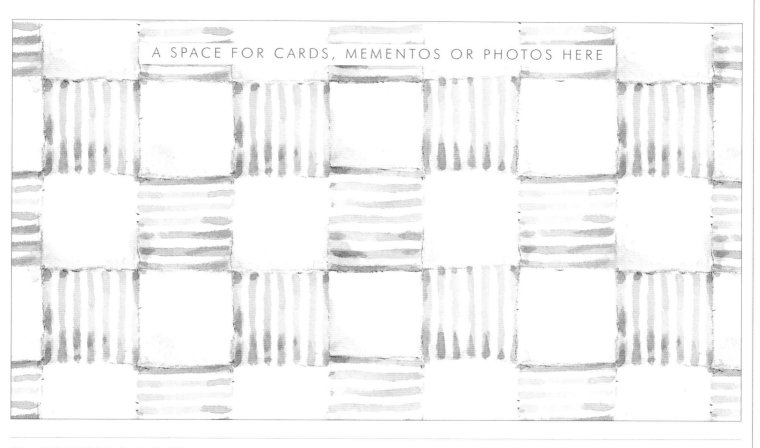

A SPACE FOR CARDS, MEMENTOS OR PHOTOS HERE

WHAT THEY SAID ABOUT YOU

MESSAGES, GIFTS AND FLOWERS

What your arrival meant to us

Family Tree

GREAT GRANDPARENTS

GREAT GRANDPARENTS

GRANDPARENTS

AUNTS AND UNCLES

PARENTS

BROTHERS AND SISTERS

BROTHERS AND SISTERS

YOU

Special relatives and family friends

Some family history

OUR FRIENDS AND FAMILY - WHAT THEY SAID ABOUT YOU AND TO YOU

YOUR PARENTS' STORY

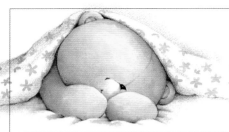

Your Mother

HER EARLY LIFE

_____
_____
_____
_____
_____
_____
_____
_____

HOW SHE FELT WHEN YOU ARRIVED

_____
_____
_____
_____
_____
_____
_____

HER DREAMS AND HOPES FOR YOU

_____
_____
_____
_____
_____
_____
_____

A SPACE FOR A PHOTO OF YOUR MOTHER

HER MESSAGE TO YOU

Your Father

HIS EARLY LIFE

HOW HE FELT WHEN YOU ARRIVED

HIS HOPES FOR YOU

HIS MESSAGE TO YOU

A SPACE FOR A PHOTO OF YOUR FATHER

Your Grandparents — about their lives

A SPACE FOR A PHOTO OF YOUR GRANDPARENTS

Messages from your Grandparents

Our Home – your room

The world when you were born

CLIPPINGS FROM MAGAZINES AND NEWSPAPERS COULD BE ADDED HERE

Firsts in the early months

GRASPED A FINGER

HELD UP YOUR HEAD

RECOGNIZED A PARENT'S VOICE

RECOGNIZED YOUR OWN NAME

SMILED

DISCOVERED YOUR OWN HANDS

SUCKED YOUR THUMB

OTHER EARLY FIRST MOMENTS

Funny moments

PHOTO HERE

Mementos

A LOCK OF HAIR	YOUR FOOTPRINT	YOUR HANDPRINT

A FEW NOTES

Things to remember

Outings

PLACES YOU WENT

FIRST VISITS TO RELATIVES, THE SEA, A PARK, THE FAIRGROUND

PLACES AND THINGS THAT DELIGHTED YOU

THE LITTLE THINGS THAT WENT WRONG

Growth chart

AGE	HEIGHT	WEIGHT
ONE WEEK		
ONE MONTH		
TWO MONTHS		
THREE MONTHS		
SIX MONTHS		
ONE YEAR		
EIGHTEEN MONTHS		
TWO YEARS		
THREE YEARS		
FOUR YEARS		
FIVE YEARS		

Special Notes

Tooth chart

1ST TOOTH	11TH TOOTH
2ND TOOTH	12TH TOOTH
3RD TOOTH	13TH TOOTH
4TH TOOTH	14TH TOOTH
5TH TOOTH	15TH TOOTH
6TH TOOTH	16TH TOOTH
7TH TOOTH	17TH TOOTH
8TH TOOTH	18TH TOOTH
9TH TOOTH	19TH TOOTH
10TH TOOTH	20TH TOOTH

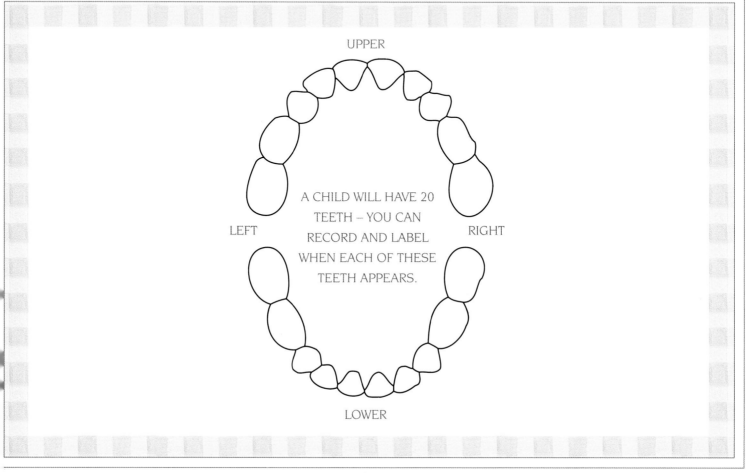

UPPER

LEFT

RIGHT

A CHILD WILL HAVE 20 TEETH – YOU CAN RECORD AND LABEL WHEN EACH OF THESE TEETH APPEARS.

LOWER

The things you loved most

PEOPLE, SONGS, TOYS, RHYMES, MUSIC – ANYTHING AND EVERYTHING

SPACE FOR A LITTLE MEMENTO

A PIECE OF YOUR CLOTHING

Your Health

DOCTOR'S VISITS	DATE
ILLNESSES	

ALLERGIES

BLOOD GROUP

IMPORTANT NOTES

A VERY IMPORTANT LIST	DATE
IMMUNIZATIONS	
MMR	
POLIO	
TETANUS	
WHOOPING COUGH	
OTHERS	

One very special day

A CHRISTENING OR NAMING DAY, OR AN IMPORTANT HAPPY DAY FOR THE FAMILY

SPACE FOR ONE OR TWO SPECIAL PHOTOS

Celebrations! Parties! Fun!

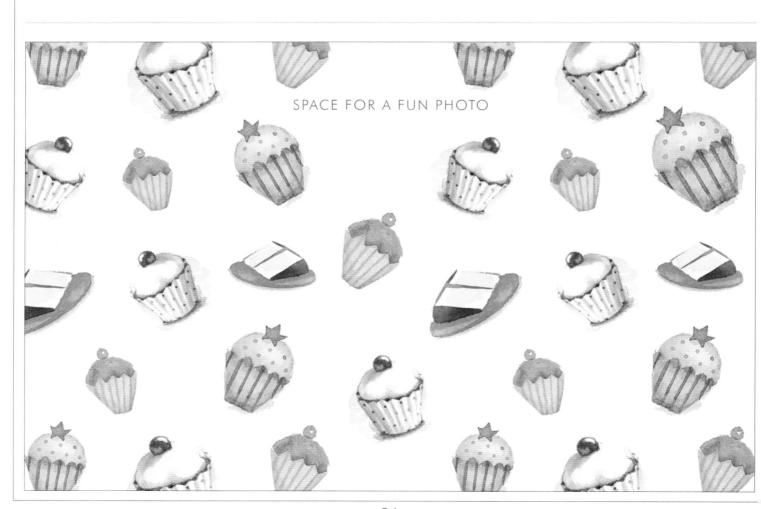

SPACE FOR A FUN PHOTO

Our family

OUR TRADITIONS, WHAT WE WERE LIKE, WHAT WE ALL DID, WHAT WE ENJOYED.

More Milestones

FIRST LAUGHED OUT LOUD

FIRST WAVED BYE-BYE

FIRST RECOGNIZED YOURSELF IN THE MIRROR

FIRST PUSHED YOURSELF UP

FIRST ROLLED OVER

FIRST CRAWLED

FIRST SAT UP BY YOURSELF

OTHER MILESTONES

First sounds and words

SPACE FOR MEMENTOS

One Year Old

PHOTO HERE

After one year — the things you loved

STORIES, SONGS, GAMES, FRIENDS

Your kind of day

...AND LITTLE THINGS WE LOVED DOING TOGETHER

PHOTO HERE

Milestones as you grew

PHOTO HERE

Things you overcame

THINGS THAT WERE SCARY!

LEAST LOVED FOOD!

SAD THINGS

THE FIRST TIMES YOU WERE NAUGHTY!

Things you were really good at

Your early drawings

GLUE PICTURES HERE

Your early writing

GLUE IN SOME EXAMPLES

54

Your first school days

YOUR FIRST DAY

YOUR TEACHERS

THINGS YOU LOVED

THINGS YOU REALLY DIDN'T LIKE

OTHER SPECIAL TIMES AT SCHOOL

Your dreams coming true

YOUR EARLY HOPES

YOUR EARLY SUCCESSES!

DIFFICULTIES YOU OVERCAME

Special moments in your childhood

Things you said

LITTLE CHILDREN SAY FUNNY THINGS...

Things we'll remember

PARENTS, GRANDPARENTS AND PEOPLE WHO LOVE YOU COULD WRITE MESSAGES HERE

Notes, photos, mementos....

Notes, photos, mementos....

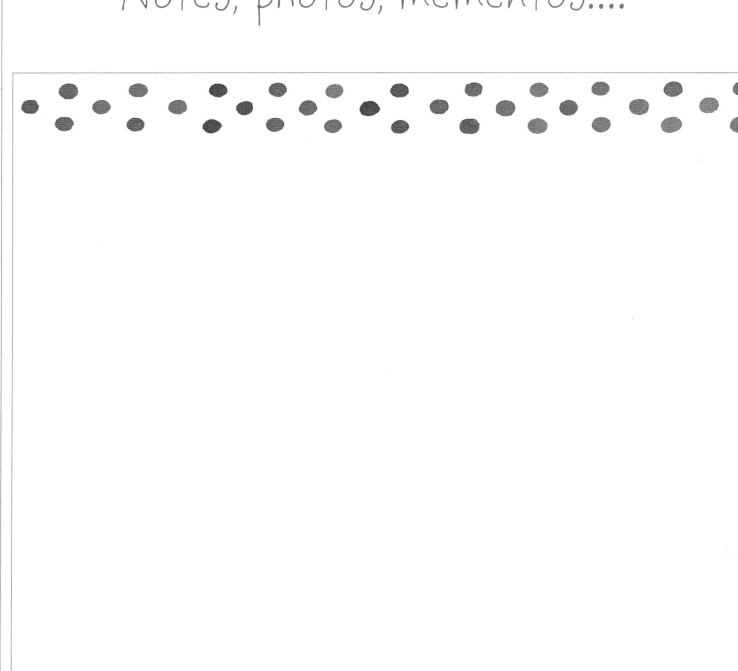